Mike,
may Haiti continue
to grow within
your heart,
and may your
heart carry you
into countries, islands
and lives
where love and
beauty
need set free.

Maktub,
Trisha-
Renee.

TOUCHING
HAITI

...a medical mission story

By Donna-Marie Hayes

Library of Congress Control Number: 2001 126634
ISBN 0-9712630-0-0

Edited by Jeanette Germain
Production assistance by
The Johnson Company Northwest, LLC
Printed by The Caxton Printers, Ltd.

Saint Alphonsus Foundation
1055 N. Curtis Road
Boise, ID 83706
208/367-2759
FAX 208/367-3967

www.saintalphonsus.org

First Edition

This publication is designed to provide information about Project Haiti,
Saint Alphonsus Regional Medical Center, Inc.'s medical mission to Haiti.
It contains the viewpoints and opinions of the author, and does not
necessarily reflect the views of Saint Alphonsus Regional Medical Center,
Inc. Further, it is distributed with the understanding that neither the author
nor the publisher is engaged in rendering medical or other professional
services.

Dedicated to
the children of Haiti.

— Table of Contents —

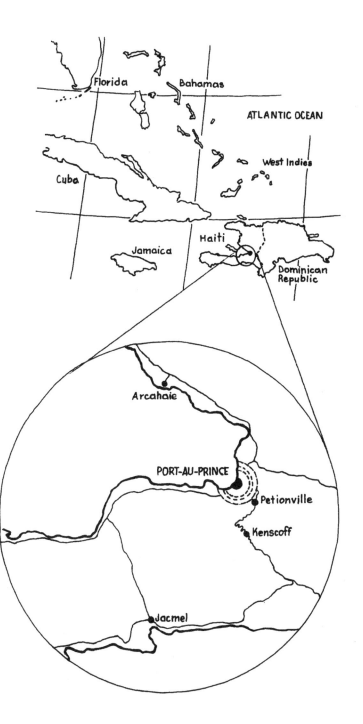

— Prologue —

He rocked back and forth, sitting upright on the small hospital bed, knees bent and head down, huddled against the stained wall for support. Taped above him was a white, water-splattered card that moved slightly with the morning breeze meandering through the room. On the card was the hand-scripted name, "Markison Frechette" and a single fly that seemed glued on purpose to the dot of the "i".

Markison's head rested between knobby knees. One thin arm cradled the bundle of his body while the other tried unsuccessfully to shield his face. Other children in the room rustled softly in their sheets, blinking wide-eyed at us as we moved past their cribs toward the boy. Open cankers the size of dimes oozed from his scalp. The cancer had spread like a fungus over his face, and both eyes were crusted shut from flesh that had taken on the appearance of a barbeque mishap. It was unbelievable. But more shocking than the sight and the awful smell, was his reaction to our approach. Markison stopped rocking and recoiled.

"Disappear, hide!" his body language screamed as he burrowed into the folds of the sheet his wounds had soiled. He had learned well that his disease labeled him a pariah, and pariahs were often beaten away.

Gently, with soft but confident words, Sister Lorraine spoke in Creole as she approached the paint-chipped bed. Unwrapping a piece of candy, she sat beside him, fumbled with the linen and placed the sweet in his mouth. She first stroked his arm, then his skinny leg.

Then she put her graying head next to his and, translating for me, said, "Markison, Markison. A doctor has come to see you."

I wasn't a doctor but the term was code for "friend," and as the boy chewed his treat, Sister gently raised his head for me to photograph.

I had come to Haiti as the token foundation board member to document the work of the Saint Alphonsus Haiti Medical Mission Team. Well-traveled among third world countries and not the squeamish type, my assignment to St. Damien's Children's Hospital on the outskirts of Port-au-Prince, seemed manageable. It would be a week of notes and picture taking — a job to go home from — an experience to be catalogued, and then I would get on with my life.

But the soul of a tortured child can't be left behind in the outrunning. It tackles the heart. That little being, that existence that says, "I am here," tumbles one's emotional defenses like the walls of Jericho. I looked at Markison and a flood of how-can-this-be's roared through my head. This was different from my childhood puppy crushed on the road; different from the ferryboat drownings I'd seen in Japan. This was certainly foreign to my pampered existence. My stomach ground with anger at his parents, at heartless people and even with God for letting this happen. Shutter clicking again and again, I hid behind the viewfinder, framing pitiful Markison and struggled with the reality.

Assignment completed, I lowered my camera — a moment too soon.

Left to capture in my heart what I wish had been on film was the bloom of Markison's open arms and the nun who so humbly filled them. Dead to the world around him, Markison had come alive with a transformation as profound as a resurrection. With lowered arms, he leaned and settled his angular body into the softness of his friend, murmuring in tandem with her the sounds of food enjoyed and comfort delivered. A fleeting smile formed across his tortured lips as his tongue played with the sweetness, and his heart finally rested in peace.

In that dimly lit room, a simple love blossomed between two people who shared little else besides their humanity. The healthy, retired, white Canadian nun looking for a purpose had found a diseased, black Haitian orphan who looked forward to nothing. From the hellhole of Markison's existence, Sister had built a trust more powerful in its simplicity than the machinations of any psychiatrist's couch.

Markison had borne the scars of a horrible disease and then the betrayal of his people, but because the men and women of St. Damien's had coaxed a fragile shred of trust from him, he emerged with his dignity intact. Under the weight of his need, all it took was a clean bed, food, care and the touch of human hands. Sister's gentleness made a visible change in Markison — a powerful change I would see manifested again and again among those who were connected by belief in the unity of humankind.

Nothing can change the inevitable. Markison will soon die at St. Damien's. But Markison won't die alone, abandoned to the gutter where he was found, unloved and covered with a filth that took days to separate from his rotting flesh. In a resigned fashion, I had to feel that Markison was one of the lucky ones.

Stepping softly from the room, I cradled my camera with a new sense of purpose. My mission in Haiti wasn't just to record diseased and abandoned little bodies; it was to witness the power of touch.

1

Forward, March

From the air Haiti looked dry and brown. Deep scars of old bauxite mines criss-crossed the bare hills beyond the city, exposing the earth to dramatic erosion. The brown cityscape spread like a murky backwater along the contour of the land and the seashore copied the same brown that dusted everything else. Only beyond the hills, the few mountains rose green.

There were nine of us on this trip, the ninth mission since 1995 when Saint Alphonsus Regional Medical Center Foundation began supporting the Haitian children's hospital and orphanage run by Father Rick Frechette. It was the maiden voyage for six of us.

We had come with various expectations underlying genuine desires to do some good. Pediatrician Dr. Matt Brown joined St. Luke's Hospital pediatric anesthesiologist Dr. Gary Cieslak and Sister Alice Mary Quintana, C.S.C., R.N., to form the medical contingent of our group. Lab technician Jay Rais and the burley microbiologist, John Burch handled hospital laboratory duties. Project Haiti team leader Debbie Hamilton, Saint Alphonsus Foundation Executive Director Annette Park, trustee Sister Agnes Anne Roberts, C.S.C., and I were the non-medical support crew.

We had met as a group for the first time the week before, to pack medical supply duffel bags in the basement of the Saint Alphonsus Regional Medical Center North Tower. Several past Haiti mission team members had come to help, and with so many hands, the sorting and customs inventory went quickly. I was struck with a sense of belonging as the veterans passed the torch with their hugs. But the weight of the project intensified with the realization that they believed our contribution was not merely important, but critical.

Except for the doctors, we had all attended the hospital "blessing" designed to buoy spirits and highlight the message in the Beatitude: "Blessed are they who have learned to find themselves in another's sorrow." Debbie, John and Sister Agnes Anne had already sharpened the lesson in Haiti, but the rest of us had yet to be tested.

Departure night at the airport was a hasty good-by at the curb, a 53-duffle bag check-in, and a hamburger dinner on the fly. The typical hurry, hurry only to wait of preflight activity left us in a tight little group in front of the farthest gate. With half of us wearing Haiti Medical Mission Team shirts, we were easy to spot. Our camaraderie just planted, we settled into the easy conversation that encourages friendships and would eventually unite our band.

To our surprise, long-time friends Brent and Julie Coles appeared, hand in hand, to send us off. Being Latter Day Saints, they were sensitive to the mission mentality. The mayor of Boise and his wife had come with a final, personal blessing of encouragement. There were hugs all around. Fortified by the unexpected gesture, we set out on the four-leg, red-eye trip to Port-au-Prince.

After the dimness of the long flight, we squinted painfully against the waves of heat from the tarmac and the bright sunlight overhead. Following Debbie down the rickety airline stairs, we wobbled to join the lines of passport-holding passengers who fluttered their official papers absentmindedly in the practiced manner of tropical islanders. Debbie returned the wave and smile from a tall man in a short sleeved, tan shirt who was patiently waiting behind the glass partition — it was Father Rick Frechette and he looked ready to get the show on the road.

Once outside Mais Gaté, Haiti's International Airport Terminal, we herded small mountains of duffel bags on luggage carts through the throng. More-than-eager young men bent on helping us for the coin or two that would feed them for the day, shouted in Creole and grabbed at our bags. With "No, merci," on our lips and "Oh, God!" in our hearts, we followed Father Rick through the melee to our transportation — a borrowed passenger van and a truck with bars on its sides and a stout lock on the door.

One touch of a bag meant a demand for compensation, and passengers without a guardian like Father Rick to help were hounded mercilessly. Debbie said this was an improvement over prior arrivals when the chaos had been allowed inside the airport. The refinement aside, there was little to do against the gauntlet and the clash of honking horns, traffic and humanity beyond.

As the poorest country in the Western Hemisphere unfolded before us, I could see evidence of how readily the most desperate of the country's 8 million inhabitants were treated as animals. Crammed into an area the size of Maryland, there were just too many of too many to sustain on a land fast becoming a desert; too many expendables.

Haiti's capital, Port-au-Prince is beyond ghetto. It transcends slum and festers like a sore. Most of the tin-roofed dwellings are four-by-eight, cinder-block hovels molded together, back-to-back and side-by-side, in a grid of open sewers that swells to overflowing when it rains. Spanned every few yards by feeble slats of wood, the ditches carry the sewage and garbage runoff of 2.5 million people.

With no toilets and no sense of personal hygiene, adults and children alike squat and leave it. Disease and filth seep into the parched earth, poisoning wells and fouling the ground. Eighty percent of Haiti's people have no clean drinking water, and few can afford the costly water that is trucked from the hills. No wonder no one sweats. They are all dehydrated. And with a 62 percent malnutrition rate, they rarely eat. It was a heartbreaking statistic made real by the gaunt bodies parading before us.

Black pigs, and skinny goats and dogs rooted in piles of stinking debris, strung out like the entrails of some disemboweled animal. Rats tilled nervously. There were no plants and no gardens. Trees had long ago vanished, victims of a million city hearths. The hot air, thick with a choking smell, shimmered in the dust of drumming feet and diesel exhaust. What was to us an assault, was orthodox for those souls who had lost the crap shoot of native birth.

I had seen overcrowded, post-flood, cholera-infected areas of Nairobi, but the density of Kenya's slums couldn't compare with Cite Soleil (City So-lay), a 2.5 square mile slum-within-a-slum of Port-au-Prince populated with 400,000 people. The whole of it was settled in the lowest part of the flatland, where open sewers converged in a last rush to the ocean. When it rained, people lived and slept on tin roofs to escape the roiling debris and raw sewage below. As storms waned, the sewers ran chocolate with precious topsoil from the hills — part of the 1 percent that is lost every year to erosion.

Even in the dark, the area shuffled and moved like a great anthill. Unable to accommodate all inhabitants prone for the night, they had to sleep in shifts. Disease-soaked hovels and their trapped existence made the wind-whipped chop of the dark ocean look pretty good. Cite Soleil was the cradle of the Boat People of Haiti.

The drive from the airport snaked past dirt streets and over main arterials that hadn't seen a road grader for years. Festooned with a political canopy of red, blue and white flags, the city's smaller streets proclaimed the return to power of Jean-Bertrand Aristide while the graffiti-covered walls and boarded windows below messaged the opposite. We sensed more than a drift of turmoil as Father Rick translated the hastily scribbled words.

Hinting at a more jubilant soul, streaks of color on wheels cut through the drabness of tattered, mud-splattered vehicles. Called Tap-Taps, the Haitian taxis were open-backed pickups, painted on the outside in bright, psychedelic colors that proclaimed a central theme, like, "Jesus Saves" or "Mama's Baby." They were like pretty beads on a string of Cheerios.

Bursting with passengers seated on benches inside, the cabs were the lifeblood of a people always on the move, bringing news, goods, passengers and whatever it was that made them who they were. The Tap-Taps were everywhere, zipping and stopping and sometimes dropping out of sight in the huge washouts that plagued the country's streets and roads. For the color alone, the Haitian taxis had my vote for national logo.

Arrival at our hotel shattered any expectation of a Spartan week in Haiti. Inside the gated compound of the El Rancho Hotel was a different world from the squalor we had seen on our way from the airport. There were manicured grounds, fountains, pools and uniformed staff; white-washed walls in spacious, air-conditioned rooms and a quiet elegance to rival Miami's hotel row. Except for the sign in the lobby that warned, "...firearms of any kind, are strictly forbidden inside this establishment," the El Rancho was a hotel with a capital H.

Seemingly unnecessary and clearly unwanted by folks signing on to a "mission," there were sound reasons for staying at the hotel. Nearby middle-class apartments were at capacity, and staying at the crowded hospital or renting one of the abutting tin-roofed hovels was not an option. Since cross-city transport for our group to various clinics, from more modest accommodations downtown, would have been costly and time consuming, the decision makers chose the alternative. It made more sense for us to hoof the short, guarded walk to the hospital each day and launch our off-site excursions in a hospital pickup driven by Father Rick.

Given the testy political situation (peppered by four bomb explosions the previous week) and Aristide's controversial inauguration in the middle of our stay, rooming at the secure hotel seemed a wise arrangement.

Close proximity also allowed us to hear daily Mass in the hospital's tiny chapel each morning and to share toast and jam breakfasts, and simple lunches with Father Rick. It was a unique opportunity, contrasting prior missions, where time spent with the priest had been limited. Daily contact was good for all of us. Debbie was thrilled that he could personally show us how much had been accomplished with so seemingly little and what more could be done with just a bit of effort.

2

Father Hen

Fourteen years earlier, Father Rick Frechette, C.P., a young Passionist priest from Connecticut, had come to manage the Haiti branch of the *Our Little Brothers and Sisters* orphanage system. Founded in 1954 by Father William Wasson, the system has served thousands of homeless children in Central and Latin American countries.

Haiti's orphanage facility, named St. Helene's after the woman who donated the 13 acre estate, was tucked high in the green folds of Kenscoff, a mountain village near Port-au-Prince. Since 1987, hundreds of children have lived safe and protected lives there.

"But with ten percent of Haiti's children dying before they reached five," said Father Rick, "we made too many trips down the mountain with dead children. I couldn't bear watching their little bodies bang against each other as I rounded the curves."

"It just wasn't right," he said, trailing his voice into a momentary silence that dredged the reality that half the deaths in Haiti each day were children under five years old.

To answer the need, a former hotel in Petionville, on the outskirts of Port-au-Prince, was converted to a place where critically ill children could be cared for, lovingly held to their last breath and gently wrapped for burial. It was the death with dignity about which we had heard so much.

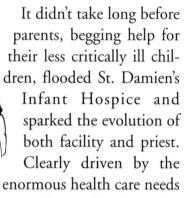

It didn't take long before parents, begging help for their less critically ill children, flooded St. Damien's Infant Hospice and sparked the evolution of both facility and priest. Clearly driven by the enormous health care needs around him, Father Rick, whose religious order is not a medical one, saw no recourse but to go back to the U.S., become a doctor himself and turn the hospice into a hospital for children.

"In Haiti there's a big difference in hospitals," said Father Rick, using both hands to illustrate the contrasts that separate Haitian hospitals from privately supported facilities.

"It is stark," he continued gravely, admonishing us further, "If you get hurt, come back here. Don't let yourself be taken to a city hospital."

He told horror stories of people lying untreated for days at a time. Yes, on admittance you'll be given a bed, but unless you have cash up front, you'll get nothing else. No sheets, no food, no doctor, no X-rays, no tests, no medication, no treatment. For good reason, the 80,000 wealthy families in Haiti (most of which live in Petionville) fly to Miami when they need medical care. Father went on to tell of seeing a man with two broken legs who had lain for days on a bare mattress, in his own excrement, begging for water and food. No one would touch him until family members scraped together money to pay for his needs.

Father Rick's St. Damien's Children's Hospital, on the other hand, provided care for 20,000 patients annually. Two thousand children a year were treated in the 100-bed, six story building that was formerly a hotel. Without running water or working elevator it was a stretch, but with a medical staff of 50 and nearly 70 other employees, the care was good and the service, clean. For the equivalent of 20 cents, mothers were motivated to travel from the far away countryside for an office visit that included an exam, laboratory tests and medication. An X-ray cost a dollar. Children admitted were fed simple meals of gruel, rice and beans, half a banana and powdered milk. Nursing mothers slept under cribs at night and, along with the staff, cared for their babies. Patient care by all family members was encouraged from 8 a.m. to 5 p.m. That explained the jungle of chairs parked next to every paint chipped bed.

The whitewashed hospital, located uphill from Port-au-Prince in Petionville, was a middle-class controversy. Humanitarian though it was, the locals resented the presence of the "undesirable poor" it attracted. One of the nearby hotels had even launched an effort to force the hospital out. On principle, our group refused to patronize their four-star restaurant.

Father Rick got a kick out of that, reminding us of the fishes-and-loaves Bible story. We wouldn't starve he assured us, and besides, Sister Philomena's desserts were better than theirs anyway.

The increased complaints from St. Damien's more tony neighbors were minimal compared to the real motivation behind Father's newest challenge. Having earned his medical degree and completed his internship, he returned in 1998 to serve Haiti's children, but then saw the expanding needs of all the poor and destitute. Soon he was making regular medical rounds at the four impromptu clinics that were run by the Brother's of Charity. With disease throughout the polluted city reaching critical mass, Father set his sights on building an immediate care hospital across the dirt road from the Brothers' clinic in Cite Soleil.

Pointing from the debris-cluttered roof of the clinic one afternoon, Father gestured toward the bare piece of land we could just see over the wall that held the sea of slums at bay.

"What we need here is a hospital, right in the heart of the slums," said Father Rick, striking the pose of an exclamation mark.

At a robust 47, we knew he had enough strength and political savvy to negotiate the minefields of a culture where corruption is king and violence commonplace. But we were unsure of our role, since his vision had grown to include men and women as well as the children who were central to our efforts. But he did convince us that this was the place to do it. (Since the most common ambulance in the slums is a wheelbarrow, one could make a case for proximity.)

— 3 —

...The Best Medicine

The first workday morning found the nine of us trudging single file from the hotel, up the tree-shaded street that bordered the grounds of the Dominican Republic embassy. Annette, Debbie and I huffed and puffed carrying unstable armloads of the nuts, chocolate and baking goodies we had brought for Sister Philomena. She loved to bake, I'd been told, and seldom had the rare ingredients. Despite our distracting cargo, we took in our surroundings.

Hundreds of folk art paintings for sale covered the walls along the way, but oddly enough, there were no hawkers around. The only other occupant was the notorious old man, Joun, who lived on a discarded seat pad under a tree. At Debbie's suggestion, we crossed to the other side, avoiding his nasty disposition and surely his smell.

Rounding the corner, we literally waded through the families and patients waiting in St.

Damien's packed courtyard. With packages
and bags hung on the cinder-block walls to
make room for the crush of people, they leaned
in a wave at our passing. As 40 pairs of eyes followed us up the stairs to the double glass doors,
Jay looked back and quipped, "Any magazines
in the waiting room?"

Crowded on rows of backless benches, their
colorful dress belied the gravity of their situation. Some of their babies would be admitted
and some would never go home. It was early
and many had been waiting since dark, with
sad, tired eyes. The tinted doors closed, blur-
ring the hues behind, and we went in to Mass,
a ritual we would come to appreciate as prepa-
ration for the day's work ahead.

The hospital chapel, a small
room on the first floor, had been
cleverly transformed into an ele-
gant and peaceful place of wor-
ship. The frosted glass windows
that faced the busy street had been
colored in stained-glass fashion with magic
markers. Filigreed metal panels hung over the
windows, deflecting noise and adding drama
to the length of the room. Along with the panels, the paper and wood screens, biblical murals
and benches had all been bartered with locals.

Even the stone altar slab had come from the yard of a neglected estate.

The expensive looking golden tabernacle was actually a handicraft box, like the ones sold on every street corner. With a can of gold spray paint and a piece of red cloth, the frugal priest had sprayed and lined the carved box, turned it sideways and mounted it on the wall. Biblical murals and statues, the work of local artists, had taken longer to create than the striking panel of woodcuts of Christ that stretched across the ceiling. Photocopied from a book, the prints were the pride of Father's interior decorating effort.

With a flourish he said, "Champagne on a beer budget. Now to prayer."

Father Rick's red vestments were a prelude to his homily, the subject of which was blood. As he spoke, soft light beamed through the filigreed windows, its rosy pattern splashing across the shiny cloth of his robe. His face and hands blushed in the warm reflection as he began.

"Blood," he said, "is an important symbol in the Church...the blood of Christ, washing away our sins, the blood of martyrs, spilled for faith...the body and blood we consume in

Communion…celebrating blood…referring to charity as the life blood of a community."

He went on about the miracle of how God had created the vast complexity of our bodies and the practical role blood played, feeding our cells and removing impurities. By the time he finished, he had made real the connection between spirituality and medicine. Small wonder he had become a doctor.

It took the rest of the morning to separate the duffle bags and haul medical supplies up and down six flights of stairs. It would take days to distribute all the supplies properly, but the grateful staff took to the chore like it was Christmas morning. Debbie made sure Father was well stocked with catheters, needles and the variety of things he would need on his rounds. Out of necessity, his medical bag was suitcase-sized.

"Why so many blue bed pads?" I asked.

"To wrap dead babies, " Debbie said sadly. "They leak," and she walked out the door.

I hadn't known. When she returned for another load, we talked about getting something better than a plastic bed pad to give to the grieving mothers. Beyond that we considered a quiet place to break the news, perhaps a storage closet somewhere, with a table and a couple of chairs, a crucifix or picture on the wall. It would be such a simple gesture with tender meaning; one more opportunity to create a poignant solution for a basic human need.

From floor to floor, I mentally catalogued potential photographs, noting important activities. The work went fast as the discharge-ready children giggled at us with every pass. Pepsodent smiles flashed without encouragement and soon we had pods of barefoot children grabbing our legs, touching our arms, to tease us to play. Later, squeals of joy echoed from the third floor as Annette gave each child a turn at blowing bubbles from the bottle she had brought. It was the perfect transition for children going home.

Cruising the open-air halls with my own followers, I got distracted by the fun and missed a humorous shot of a bare-bottomed four-year-old, pushing his toy truck along the floor.

"Damn, I missed it."

"Me, too," laughed Annette from behind.

The fourth floor was a less jovial place. The hospital morgue was at the end of the hall, behind a closed door where sunlight never reached. At the other end was Markison and in one of the middle rooms, was the little girl whose reddened eyes bulged past eyelids, completely out of her head. Matt and Gary diagnosed a cancerous tumor, pushing behind the eyes. Her beautiful mother held the child tenderly, giving futile comfort. They had been there for days, and the growth had only worsened. There was little hope, but as I passed by the shaded room, she beckoned me in. As though somehow my taking her daughter's picture would help, she positioned the child on her hip and smiled.

My camera was a heavy, Nikon F with an 80-200 lens that looked like it meant business. An old workhorse, it had been my companion for a quarter century, and I hefted it with respect, comfortable with its manual aspects and confident that it would take good pictures. The camera had available light limitations, but that would not be a problem in the sunlit hospital.

Sister Lorraine tapped me on the shoulder and asked if I would take her picture with Francesca, the tiny HIV baby down the hall. I knew Sister would be leaving soon, to continue her ministry search; that she simply wanted a remembrance of someone special.

Above Francesca's plastic bassinette, the card read "Francesca Frechette."

"Sister," I asked dumbly, "is she related to Markison?"

Sister's face took on that look people get just before they tell a touching story. She explained that all the foundlings had been given Father Rick's last name. He had felt it important that they have a family name, so gave them his.

She lifted tiny Francesca and cradled her, coaxing a nearly imperceptible smile from the infant's pale lips. Struck by the tiny, seeking fingers as she tested Sister's hand, and her wide, probing eyes, I felt like cheering Francesca on, encouraging her to respond for posterity. I snapped the shot and moved on.

Electricity and water are things we take for granted in the U.S. In Haiti, both are luxuries and intermittent at best. Take toilet procedures. Each bathroom in the hospital had a 5 or 10 gallon bucket of water, which had to be hauled up stairs and replenished when empty. The standard rule was: if it's yellow, let it mellow, if it's brown, flush it down. Used toilet paper went in a separate wastebasket because it plugged septic tanks or the more common sewage cisterns that leached into the ground. After each flush, water in the tank was replaced with a pan full of water from the large bucket, making the toilet ready for the next user. Every room had soap and a water basin, and clean towels, crisp from the line. We washed often and as a habit, kept little bottles of antiseptic hand wash in our pockets for backup.

Limitations of water, supplies and mobility aside, patients and staff at St. Damien's felt grateful to be there. Dr. Jacqueline Gautier, the hospital's medical administrator, ran a tight ship, making best use of the medical supplies and systems development support supplied by the Saint Alphonsus Foundation. Her modest salary, though comparable for Haitian physicians, was barely minimum wage by U.S. standards and was hardly what kept her there. Like Father Rick, she and the other paid staff shared an allegiance to the little hospital and had stayed with the hope that services at the hospital would continue to improve.

Across from the hospital was a cyber café where, for a pittance, we could e-mail home. In the small windowless, upstairs room, were six computer terminals and an oscillating fan that annoyingly shuffled papers more than it cooled. I was focused on a dog-eared poster I couldn't read and listening to the clicks and taps of the others, when the French nun finished her report and left with a nod of her veiled head. Hunched over the warmed keyboard and determined to ignore the sweltering heat, I beat out my first message.

"Hello from Haiti...Day one began with Mass in the tiny hospital chapel and quickly filled with experiences to defy description..." I typed, as the sweat trickled through my hair and evaporated to a crust before it could drip on the keys.

It was dusk when we left the heat of the café for the cooler air of the street. With the change, I shivered, and my skin raised goose bumps that lasted halfway down the road to the hotel. The old man, Joun, was in a fetal position on his mat when we walked by. Drool dripped from one side of his mouth, and his sock-less but shoed foot rested in the dirt. Once, we were told, he had been a hawker.

Refreshed by showers and the evening air, our team gathered by the pool. We swapped stories and fell into the sick humor medical folks invent to stay sane. Both irreverent and healing, it was an experience quickly appreciated by all, including the nuns. Fairly fleshy exchanges escalated then suddenly stopped, hanging in the silence of uncertainty. Maybe Sisters Alice Mary and Agnes Anne might be offended — the unexpected question sat on the table for a split second, then brought a, "Naw!" and a hearty, infectious laugh from Matt. My laugh ignited the nagging cough I had developed and, teasing me, they asked a passing waiter if there was a doctor in the house.

On one of our excursions to reality, we numbered some of the simple things the hospital needed. More maintenance-dependent equipment would be out, as would materials that wouldn't survive the humid heat. Jay suggested glass slides for the laboratory. Thinking back to my basic biology class, I couldn't imagine a lab *without* slides. Good Lord!

John chimed in with his appreciation for the new lab air conditioner since he'd suggested it last time around. I'd never given much thought to tissue and blood samples shriveling before they could be examined. His current concern centered on the limited refrigerator storage space, and just who back home could fix the things the hospital staff and volunteers could not. Practical solutions took some planning.

Cuban cigars followed an unremarkable hotel dinner and poolside conversation resumed. John volunteered how much he liked coming to Haiti.

"It clears your mind from hospital trivia," he confided.

"True," said Sister Agnes Anne, "everywhere it's pretty basic. What's truly amazing is that the people here, in the most deplorable conditions, still have faith."

Sister wasn't talking about any particular religion. We knew that Haitians had invented Voodoo, a religion rich in expression and soulful in its meaning. Its true practice was tame and deeply spiritual; not the nonsense that Hollywood spewed. Other signs of spirituality were surprising in the context. We had seen colorfully dressed children, marching up the roads with their parents on Sunday morning. Bibles in hand, they came out from the rubble, like so many butterflies emerging from a drab chrysalis. We wondered how they managed cleanliness and style in all that mess and how they could maintain such pride in their culture and dignity in their bearing.

"They're a remarkable people," Sister finished with the voice of experience.

In the shadow of a palm under the full, tropical moon, we settled back in our chairs and peered up at the stars. Gary, the group's loner, retired early, leaving our poolside sociology,

armchair psychology group in the soon-to-van-
ish quiet.

4

On Edge

Tuesday dawned to clear skies and nervous activity around the hotel. Squeaky housekeeping carts and the swish, swish of natural palm brooms beat a rhythm against the background of clinking glasses. Even the paintings lining the street to the hospital seemed loud as we passed not one, but two armed security guards. The open embassy gate framed a spy-movie scene of several large, shiny cars with blackened windows and a helicopter gracing the lawn. Two men in dark suits and sunglasses walked toward us, taking deep drags on their cigarettes. They managed "Hola" and a nod as they passed us on their way to the hotel.

At the hospital, we met Dr. Malherbe and Astrid.

Dr. Malherbe Desert (De-zer) is a Haitian physician serving St. Damien's and St. Helene's Orphanage on a modest contract salary from our foundation. He made clinic rounds with Father Rick, assisted the priest as a church deacon and supported an active family of five young children. He always greeted us with a wide smile and the whisper of a bow.

Astrid, an attractive, young blond woman, is a familiar volunteer who helps Father on his rounds. She is an educated, blue-eyed beauty in her mid-20's. What on earth was she doing traipsing around Haiti? Like the dozens of volunteers that webbed the wasted country, she had come to do what she could and stayed. Some day, she said, she'd marry her World Health Organization bureaucrat fiancé, settle down and raise a family. Right then, however, there was work to do — a common theme among those in the trenches. She is not formally trained in medicine, but as we were to discover in Haiti, that shortcoming doesn't matter.

Following Mass we split up, with Debbie cataloguing medical supplies and resourceful Jay and John repairing equipment in the hospital lab. The rest of us were to accompany Father Rick, first to the Sisters of Charity Sans Fils Home for the Dying and then to one of the Brothers' clinics in Cite Soleil.

Shouldering our packs, we walked past the hawkers stationed on the hospital corner to the waiting pickup. Thin and hungry looking, they had the beseeching eyes that seemed Haiti's hallmark. The old woman selling brooms caught my attention and for some reason, I imagined her outstretched hand a conduit to a grandchild at home. I had nothing to give her but silent concern. It was a disquieting feeling that lingered through the ride to Sans Fils.

The Sisters of Charity wore the familiar blue-trimmed robes of their order's founder, Mother Theresa. Already sweating in the morning heat, we marveled that they could look so cool and clean as they hauled buckets of water and scrubbed and labored. Trailing behind one of them, I peeked into the supply room, curious about what medicines they had. Stacked on shelves behind a white sheet and neatly labeled were huge bottles of Valium, Prozac and something that simply read Strong Pain Killers.

The Sisters lived the simple life of their order, caring for the dying and abandoned by day and praying quietly in the tiny chapel of their modest convent at night. On the wall in a narrow hallway was a two-by-three-foot board, brown with age. Rows and rows of carefully written names were on it, accompanied by the origins and death dates of all the Sisters who had served at the hospice. Mother Theresa's name was there. The tired board was almost full and so were the Sisters' wards.

The quiet, spotless facility housed terminally ill men and women, and on that day, three incredibly tiny newborns. Bundled side by side under a netted cover designed to keep flies off food, they lay peacefully oblivious to their future. All had HIV-positive mothers, an indication of the rapid growth of AIDS in Haiti. The Sisters seemed so joyful about the births in the face of imminent death. As I held one of the trembling infants, a passing nun, arms loaded with clean sheets, leaned down to brush her cheek against the baby's head, and smiling reverently, was off.

One of the Sisters from India told us, "It is so much worse here. In India, people shared what little they had. In Haiti, there is nothing to share."

Dormitory-style rows of cots spread across spotless floors in the women's ward. Sunlight through the doors cast shadows under the freshly made cots, hiding random combs and a few pink bottles that lay beneath. Small bundles of clothes and personal items tucked at the head of each cot served as pillows for the blue-gowned women at rest. There were no books or magazines, evidence of Haiti's 85 percent illiteracy rate, and only one young visitor, a frightened looking girl, hovered over a woman who labored with audible breaths.

Half of the women moved slowly about the room whispering when whispered to, floating baby blue through the sunbeams. The rest were prone, measuring movement to available energy. We, the untrained, had come to help. We hardly knew where to start.

Without permission to photograph, I joined Annette and Sister Agnes Anne in the lotion brigade. Equipped with gloves and bottles, we moistened dry, thin skin, giving comfort to women who methodically and nonchalantly bared themselves to strangers. Our touch was welcomed silently and reflectively, rather like an anointing. Every deliberate move hung in the air and seemed to form a dramatic meaning for someone. Their eyes followed us, absorbing the moment as readily as their skin did the lotion. When my bottle emptied, I simply held their hands and stroked their hair and, having done such a little thing, felt unworthy of the gratitude in their eyes. Sister Agnes Anne blessed each one in turn, and the few who responded in recognition made her smile.

The faces of the women seemed not to match the shriveled bodies we attended. Perhaps it was resolution that molded their large luminous eyes, smooth features and chocolate skin into beauty. Iridescent nail polish at the ends of long sensuous fingers surprised me — the gift of a volunteer who came every other week to do manicures and pedicures. Likewise, a well-dressed gentleman was giving shaves and haircuts to male patients on the day we visited and he smiled at us as we scrutinized his work.

Watching some of the stronger women braid and style each other's hair, I was reminded of the Saint Alphonsus nurse who gently combed and braided my mother-in-law's hair just before she died. I wouldn't have thought to do that. I hadn't known then that looking good, even in the final transition, was important.

Back on the road, Father answered our "after-death" questions in graphic detail. I pictured the city's morgues in Holocaust hues, so many stiff bodies stacked haphazardly in lightless, airless hospital rooms or wherever space could be found. Mothers, he said, have to search through the naked mass for children who had died in the night. Families lucky enough to find their loved ones had a burial problem. With not enough room for the living, the dead had few options. Even the compassionate Sisters and Brothers struggled with pragmatic solutions of disposal, straining against the deluge of a resigned and callous population.

Graves and caskets had to be rented, and, after the allotted time, the bodies were removed and taken to mass graves by the sea. With each rain, erosion exposed the bodies to vultures and dogs, scattering the bones and churning the whole of the human compost pile. Caskets too were recycled — or stolen for firewood.

Father Rick's words haunted me as we passed hundreds of ghostly pedestrians, barely visible through the slum dust. Although his descriptions provoked a sense of futility — a primitive emotion that matched our destitute surroundings — his delivery seemed a call to arms. It was Tuesday morning and already things were heating up.

Traveling through Port-au-Prince in the white pickup, six crowded in the cab and the rest precariously perched in the open back, we must have cut quite a picture. White faces in a sea of black, dressed in blue scrubs and identified by the computer printout of a green hospital cross, taped to the windshield. We were the minority in a culture where the worth of a man depends on the creaminess of his skin and his ability to speak French. As dark faces flashed by my window, I wondered how they could know we weren't people turned blind by an overdose of power, comfort and endless luxuries.

By prior arrangement, Father Rick detoured to a gas station where a young, blond man, backpack slung over his shoulder, stood waiting. He was Irish and had come to Haiti to look up some nuns from his village. As I came to know, the network of volunteers in Haiti is wide and no willing hands are turned away, least of all, from the neighborhood clinics the Brothers ran on a shoestring. Up he hopped into the truck, happy to join our troop.

We turned a corner and lurched past the usual collage of stalls and hovels, avoiding piles of garbage and three barefoot men struggling to cart half a car body through the canyons of the alley. By this time, the folks in the back were suffering with the hot, gritty wind that blew homemade kites nearly horizontal across the road. Through squinty eyes they spotted the crowd down the road, whose self-appointed task was to herald our arrival at the Brothers' clinic with shouts and loud slaps on the rust colored gate.

The gate opened on Haitian time and we entered in a cloud of dust that rolled out into an open, coral-gravel clearing. Ringed with rambling buildings, the compound was contained by a 20-foot, broken glass and shard-topped wall, woven with razor wire that sparkled in the sun. Here, too, security was at a premium as desperate patients vied to get in, and the Brothers struggled to defend their sun-bleached buildings against predators. Thievery created life and death choices for everyone.

Father turned off the motor and we sat silent in the quiet, with shuffling sounds from the hushed crowd muffled behind the gate. This sun-bleached place was also for the dying.

One of the Brothers in dusty, gray pants and a striped shirt approached with a list of patients for the doctors to see, then directed attention to the most critical case.

Needing immediate care was a young man with a broken back who had been found beside a road, the victim first of a car accident and then of abandonment. Brought to the clinic by one of the other Brothers, he lay naked on a plastic sheet, face up, his legs twitching, his body sculpted by light from the single open door at the end of the room.

The spasms, just one symptom of his injuries, continued while the doctors determined the gravity of his paralysis. His nonfunctioning bladder had swelled to watermelon-size, and the man could barely breathe from the weight and pressure.

Relieving the bladder would require using a large needle pushed through the abdominal wall to drain the urine through a catheter. Antibiotics injected directly into the organ might improve the blockage, but the condition would most likely return. With scissors and a flashlight handy in my backpack, I was conscripted to help in the dimly lit room.

Gauging bladder position and required depth, Gary took a deep breath, gave a firm shove and set the needle. He bent awkwardly over his patient on the low cot and holding the needle, repeatedly emptied the urine-filled syringe into the shallow pan Father held. It took a long time in that uncomfortable position, but Gary never wavered.

Procedure completed, Sister Alice Mary inserted another catheter and suggested using a spent saline solution bag as a collection unit instead of the open pan. Necessity being the mother of invention, the contraption was attached. It seemed everything in Haiti led multiple lives.

The rest of that morning and into the afternoon, similar scenes played out against a backdrop of tidy, but hardly sterile, naturally lit rooms. There were no curtains for privacy or for windows, and though relatives had come to vigil the dying, it was quiet. I got a faint whiff of cough syrup from the gallon jug on the windowsill — a unique air freshener. Except for the occasional religious picture, the walls were bare.

Ol' Mother Hubbard would have been at home in the Brothers' supply room. Relying mostly on the medication and equipment from Father Rick's oversized black bag, the Brothers functioned with alcohol swabs, a few scattered bottles of medicine and rolls of donated cloth for bandages. Although the Brothers were not trained as doctors and their supplies were wanting, their clinic was appreciated because of their legendary compassion. In a dim corner I glimpsed the young Irishman, on his knees feeding one of the older patients, who was propped in a wheel chair. The compassion was contagious.

The near noon light turned harsh as Annette, Sister Agnes Anne and I made our way through the hospice wards of men. Weakened with tuberculosis, hepatitis and AIDS, they lay nearly naked on cots, silently watching us watch them. For me, it was less watching and more seeing — how people, joined in communal death, dealt so respectfully with one another.

Like the women we comforted at the Sisters, these men spoke with their eyes of a pride that echoed Markison's "I am here," and a deep gratitude for the touch of human hands. More than one man followed slowly the trail of my latex-gloved hand as I spread lotion across his sad limbs. Responding to gentleness, they breathed deep, soulful breaths, recording with all their senses, the now-rare connection of simple touch. Each one, with nowhere to go but gone, patiently waited his turn. We kept hearing, "These are the lucky ones," rescued from neglect to live whatever time left among people who cared. The premise was simple yet epic. One man at a time, they were freely offered peace to prepare.

Twice a week, the clinic opened to treat the general poor, who queued up, waiting on benches under a tin-roofed, open-air hall to be seen by Father and whatever traveling medical folks he had in tow. An old, life-sized crucifix hung above the raised stage, facing a crowd that was seated in a dozen neat rows. Examinations were public affairs, and with three docs at work, the serious audience had plenty to see.

Annoying flies buzzed in reconnaissance in small clouds above our heads. Dust, kicked up by the breeze in the clearing, swirled gracefully in the sunlight. It was a hushed atmosphere, broken only by the whimpers of small children, the shuffling of feet on the concrete floor and periodic groans from a boy of about eight. He had a painful abscess the size of a large orange on his chest. The mound was shiny and smooth from the taut skin that stretched above his ribcage, and the whole area looked hot and tender.

Selected for surgery, the barefoot boy and his father crossed the gravel to the main hospice, where Father and Gary prepared the anesthetic. For the frightened boy, seeing the menacing looking I.V. made his anxiety nearly equal to the pain. Showing her trademark sensitivity, Astrid gathered the frightened child in her arms as he squirmed on the tattered gurney and looked reassuringly into his face. She cocked her head and smiled. It was the last thing he saw until he woke up, groggy but minus the abscess.

The dark, worried faces of Gary's surgical audience soon flashed white with smiles. One of the Brothers gave instructions in Creole, and clutching a packet of antibiotics, the father nodded gratefully to each of us and half carried his wobbly boy out the gate.

The afternoon wore on, as docs performed surgery in the open-air porch while I took advantage of the light.

Drawn by a shadow that cut diagonally across a white wall, I spied an old man shuffling blindly past me. Singing the mantra we had heard all morning, and leaning on his staff for balance, he sat down exactly at the junction of the shadow, the bright green, wainscoted wall and the corrugated tin door behind. I snapped the picture with studied confidence and turned in search of other models on the porch who would stand out against the building's starkness.

Eager to have me take his picture, a teenaged helper who lived at the clinic beckoned with a broad smile. I positioned him along the same green wall and expected a common mug shot of a grinning boy. He had a different idea. Carefully striking his pose, he lifted his chin and looked straight in my lens. The smile was gone, replaced by features that traced on his blue-black face, great pride in his survival and confidence that his incredible luck would hold. I hoped it was prophetic.

Suddenly, a Brother announced that we should leave, before 3 p.m. when the streets would be blocked and we *wouldn't* get out.

The anticipated political demonstrations had begun. We moved quickly, with Father executing a circuitous return to the hospital, nicely avoiding the smoldering, smelly barricades of tires and trash. It was flat-out confusion, with all the dust and fumes and honking and shouting of a mega traffic jam. Nobody wanted to get caught in the demonstration. The normal ebbs and flows of intersections slowed to a trickle as anxious drivers refused to give way. We seemed suspended in time with a hurricane of anger swirling around us and I was worried about the others exposed in the back of the pickup. Leaving the chaos behind came none too soon.

It was much calmer in the hospital neighborhood although a contributing factor was that the power had gone out, rendering, among other things, the cyber café useless. A common nuisance, power outages were the bane of developing countries, changing the flow of life, redirecting activity to alternate modes. I would work on my own plan "B" later and headed back across the empty street to the hospital for a late lunch.

The others were resting their weary bodies across furniture and held open cans of cool pop in their hands by the time I got to the sixth floor. Lunch was on its way and our hungry band was just settling in when a helicopter flew up to and around the hospital. To the delight of the children on the other side, it hovered a bit and landed behind a clump of trees, somewhere between them and the El Rancho. I lost sight of it behind the rows of laundry on the roof.

"Thwack, thwack, thwack," circled the second helicopter. With us in scrubs, the smell of the hospital and the pounding memory of real live operations in my head, I couldn't help but think of the old TV show, "MASH." Father seemed unconcerned but said little about what was clearly a novel happening. There was caution in the air. We waited for a while reviewing the day, covered our options and headed for the hotel.

The previously empty hotel parking lot was full of cars and buses; our second clue that something was up. The place was full of people, mostly men in suits, carrying briefcases and cell phones. Serious-looking armed soldiers in crisp tan uniforms wandered by twos through the groups, the smell of gun oil wafting behind. It was no time to linger.

From our balcony we watched as pockets of men gathered and dispersed. Not a party atmosphere, there were few women and no food or drinks to be seen. They looked hot and business-like behind sunglasses that flashed like fishing lures as they milled around the pools. Busy media types aimed their bright lights and cameras in our direction, the object of their attention being the room below us.

Anxious to e-mail my husband, Bob, I "Bonjour'd" my way to the hotel office where I'd worked a deal to use their computer, which was tucked in a dark corner at the back of an unlit room. (Bribery works every time.) From that vantage I could see the front desk from behind and counted one tall and portly general (with a chest full of medals, he had to be a general) and two other officers who alternated between wide smiles for the pretty receptionist and glowering looks everywhere else.

"Keep your head down and your back against the wall," had been my husband's pre-trip prescription. I kept it in mind.

Concentrating so intently on the e-mail message home, I wasn't immediately aware of not being alone. In my peripheral vision, the watcher moved ever so slightly, breaking a train of thought that focused on my uniquely hidden position. I was being watched by a small brown gecko, which had emerged from behind the picture on the wall next to my head. He was close enough for me to see his sticky toes and the half-open mouth, glistening with moisture. I smiled and asked in a whisper if he was a spy on the wall or perhaps in the employ of one of the army of reporters wandering about. He only blinked.

It was late afternoon by the time we showered and ordered one of the hotel's cool, fruit drinks. We stayed in our rooms and expected whatever was happening would end by 5 or 6 p.m. But politics, not being a 9 to 5 affair, stayed the course. We dined through the lights, cameras…but no action. Only the rumbling of a hundred low voices that kept us awake all night. Finally, about 3 a.m., the mystery-group went home, and the cleanup crew arrived.

5

Lying Low

Wednesday, February 7, 2001, was Inauguration Day for Jean-Bertrand Aristide, activist priest turned domesticated politician. Duly elected president in 1990, Aristide's support had soured well before the bloody military coup d'etat, his exile and his subsequent return in 1994. The opposition had boycotted his recent election and boldly threatened establishment politicians, journalists and clerics, vowing to turn "their blood to ink, their skin to parchment and their skulls to inkwells." It sounded like strong, Hollywood Voodoo stuff to me and I was glad we were lying low at the hospital.

To my question about clerics being in danger, Father shrugged and said the current situation was nothing new, just much worse in the last five years. Government corruption, coupled with drug lords fighting over turf, was a way of life. There were traffickers everywhere, most with their own armies of thugs. The conflicts even had some people calling to reinstate Haiti's military, which had ushered in an era of human rights abuses and dictatorship and was later forced out by the U.S. Innocent people caught in the crossfire of lawlessness had no recourse. My family, I said, knew that first-hand.

His face grew serious as I related how, in 1986, my brother-in-law's older brother, Paul Alexander, had been murdered by an intruder just 48 hours before he was to leave Port-au-Prince. A World Health Organization doctor, Paul had given his life to third world countries, and had been shot in the heart for the effort. "Baby Doc" Duvalier had just fled the country with $60 million in his pocket, and the government was no more able or willing to render justice then than it was today. Family phone calls nearly melted the lines with objections when they learned of my mission to Haiti.

From the patio off the sixth-floor staff room, we could see the nearly empty streets that fanned eastward toward the hills where the wealthy lived. Earth-colored houses, stacked on each other like the Anasazi cliff dwellings of New Mexico, reached up for fuel, for space, for air. Foliage perished in the advance, leaving an unsustainable wasteland that would soon meet the guarded walls of hoarded lands. Would the lines hold?

Through the lattice brick wall that defined the hospital laundry flashed newly washed sheets and the occasional pop of color from a laun- dress' clothing. They were a cheery bunch, scrubbing and wringing by hand and smiling for my camera. The air had that special smell of damp wash hung out to dry in a sunny breeze. I wanted to photograph the rows of drying laundry from above, so Father suggested scaling the wall to stand on the flat-topped roof.

What a perspective. Nose to nose with the hospital's 10-foot high green cross, the 360-degree rooftop view offered some interesting shots and a great vantage for watching the intrigue below. On one side, three bare-chested men playing dominoes could be seen through the roof of their shanty; on the other, a row of uniformed guards.

The policemen securing the hotel and embassy street shifted from foot to foot in ennui. It must have been all that scuffling that attracted a passing shoeshine boy who crab-walked his way down the line of men. In due time, the cavalcade appeared — police on motorcycles, flashing lights, the big, dark cars we had seen earlier, an ambulance, a truck, several marked and unmarked cars, and a bit later, the helicopter again.

At noon, we watched the Inauguration Mass on TV, Father translating the bishop's serious homily and interpreting political posturing outsiders would miss. The bishop pulled no punches, admonishing Aristide "...to see his people, on their knees, begging for help...at the very least, give them roads," a direct reference to the infrastructure projects that $2.3 billion in foreign aid had failed to deliver.

Father was clearly disappointed with Aristide but careful with his comments. Sister Lorraine was more hopeful. The rest of us couldn't imagine how anything less than a miracle would do any good.

The elaborate ceremony was a somber contrast to more celebratory U.S. inaugurations. In Haiti, there were few smiles. Dour-faced dignitaries sat through the new leader's televised speech of grandiose promises delivered in French, Creole, and Spanish. At the end of the speech, a government commercial showed primitive animation of stage curtains parting to reveal a beaming Aristide, flanked by doves and Haitian flags. The broadcast never mentioned the opposition.

Reaching for his third brownie, Father Rick talked more about the corruption that interferes with daily life. When two hospital trucks were stolen, the police were no help. Upon the third theft, Father alerted the police but set about to find the truck on his own. Miraculously, he did, and called the authorities to cancel their search. The police promptly arrived to confiscate the truck, for "evidence." Learning that the hospital would then have to pay $1,000 for its return, Father delivered a stern homily and, suiting action to word, got in the would-be hostage truck and drove off.

I spent a lot of time dogging Dr. Matt that day as he wandered down to play doctor. Matt was always fun and reminded me of my oldest son, right down to his insatiable interest in food. Slyly complimentary of Sister Philomena's many cookies, Matt was never without a Pop Tart or two squirreled in the bottom of his medical bag. With his ready, infectious laugh and big-kid demeanor, he brought lightness to heavy work. It was good medicine to have him around, and the children loved him. For Matt, language was no barrier as he poked and prodded and focused his smile on each patient. He was one of my favorites.

Sister Lorraine's Francesca had become another of my favorites. I visited her at every opportunity, trying to replace the nun who had moved on in her search. The infant followed my eyes and voice and clung to offered fingers, with delicate hands that reminded me of piano players or Balinese dancers. She pursed her lips and rooted as my babies had done, but never cried. One of the staff came in to check diapers and I left for the lounge and more inauguration talk.

It was much later we learned that "...the opposition, known as Convergence, had met with Aristide at an undisclosed location, well into the early morning hours the night before ...that they were unsuccessful in reaching political compromise...that the opposition had elected their own president in a parallel government...Haiti was headed to more difficult and uncertain times..." There was talk of civil war.

"Rats," I mumbled. As a news junkie and self-confessed "happening" addict, I lamented the only tangible souvenir I had was an undeveloped photograph of Aristide's helicopter.

6

Family Matters

The next morning Astrid briefly joined us for toast at the hospital. Partnered the last two days with Gary, she had proven invaluable, translating for examinations and comforting each patient with her famous direct look and firm touch or caress when things got scary. Since Father had delayed our morning trip to the orphanage to visit with a Haitian doctor, we welcomed the chance to enjoy her company.

The conversation between the two doctors was another glimpse into the commonplace behavior of a lawless society. Having just saved a man's life from a gunshot wound, the doctor had been "strongly advised" by the patient to join him in a scheme to bilk the insurance company out of a payment that Father had already covered. Instead of being grateful, the man resorted to threats and graft. The mentality of "dog biting the hand that feeds it" was beginning to complicate both random and planned acts of mercy to the point of frustration. We were all ready to hear a different tune.

The long-awaited 10-mile trip to the orphanage in Kenskoff lived up to the harrowing stories I'd heard. Whoever laid out the road up the mountain was downright inept. Corners were banked to send vehicles flying over the edge, and the thin pavement only encouraged speed. Washouts and potholes competed with piles of intended fill. Kamikaze drivers dodged all of it with little regard for pedestrians. With both hands on the wheel, Father was respectful of a road that had just taken the life of a board member and friend.

Winding up 3,000 feet, the road accessed humble farms and the gated properties of Haiti's elite. It is less populated in the mountains, but the sharp class division remained. Petty criminals and high-priced thugs work at any elevation, and it may look and smell better, but only by degrees.

We lunched halfway up the road at the Baptist Mission of Haiti, a handicraft cooperative and Americanized restaurant. It had been a popular oasis for the United Nations contingent that just pulled out of Haiti two days before. The user-friendly shop in the mission compound was a relief from the persistent and sometimes rude hawkers across the road. Turned backs and wagging fingers made it clear that picture taking was out, so I hid the camera and went to lunch with the others.

The Subway knock-offs were so filling that I wrapped what I couldn't eat and stowed it for the old lady who sold brooms in front of the hospital. Matt ordered a banana split with six spoons. Recharged by the cool sweetness of the treat, we gathered our purchases, piled back in the pickup and continued on up the mountain.

One look at the faces grinning into my lens confirmed that St. Helene's Orphanage of the *Nos Petits Freres at Poeurs* (Little Brothers and Sisters) was the silver lining in Haiti's dark cloud. Ten miles above a rotting Port-au-Prince we breathed deeply, a sweet and cool air that rose from the shade of trees, a hundred feet tall. It looked like the Oregon summer camp my daughter enjoyed.

Patches of sunlight flashed with running children as sounds of recitation floated from the four-story school. I stopped to photo-graph a preschooler hanging out her wash and was instantly caught by a gaggle of nearby toddlers. Like their older sisters, the girls had bouquets of barrettes in their hair, scattered without concern for shape, color or even necessity. The display was a charming and fun cap on their sweet faces.

Saved by Sister Agnes Anne and her bottle of bubbles, I wandered alone to the "special needs" house where I was bear-hugged by a retarded 12-year-old boy, who knew exactly where I, with my camera, should go. To the rooftop he led me, where their teacher, Gena, held court to four smiling children, sunning themselves in wheelchairs. Actually there were five, because one child cradled a smaller one with sunken, useless eyes.

Gena had been a special needs teacher at the orphanage for four years and she clearly relished the chance to show off her pupils. Mid-sentence, she was startled at an impish poke from a Down-syndrome girl and remarked how "...they were a joy — being here is a blessing for me," she beamed. Having raised a special needs child myself, I couldn't imagine having two dozen of them at once. On the second floor were youngsters in their own separate worlds. Totally dependent, they would live their lives, clean and nurtured by a handful of dedicated people.

Most Haitian children, whose families could afford school, wore uniforms, but the "little brothers and sisters" of school age had other options. Each morning they chose from a common closet the clothes they would wear that day, making the orphanage look like any American campus. With T-shirts flagging familiar logos, it was easy to see where the bulk of the clothes originated. It's too bad the donors back home couldn't see how proudly the children wore them. Toys were shared and chores assigned accordingly. Lessons were taught in the mornings and mandatory, supervised study sessions followed. Governed by the sunlight, bedtime was early.

Each of us had brought things for the children, and though toys and clothes had to be warehoused, I used a small jar of pink iridescent body paint to liven things up. Like teenage girls everywhere, they rubbed tentative fingers across their cheeks and giggled approval. Arm in arm they wandered off, whispering and glowing with female secrets while the boys watched with that familiar sideways glance that heralds puberty. There was none of the middle-school cootie factor I'd seen when I'd tried to pose some girls with a cluster of boys. "Oh, oh," I thought. "Father certainly has his hands full."

The neat orphanage grounds sprawled on a gradual slope toward a stone chapel at the edge of an emerald canyon where the wind played high in trees. Lush and fertile, it was an enviable part of the 2 percent of Haiti that still has trees. Transformed from an estate to a refuge for homeless children, only the swimming pool sat unused, brackish with green rainwater, hinting at the luxury of a previous life.

St. Helene's is an orphanage where, by design, adoption is not an option. Based on his experience with scarce adoptions and fragile emotions, and troubled by the realization that "only the cute ones get picked," the founding Father made the decision that all the children should live as one family, in separate cottages of 20 or so, attended by a "house parent." The children are nourished, body and soul, and educated as the hope of Haiti. Each is asked to return for a year of service at one of the Little Brothers and Sisters facilities. Father Rick was understandably proud of the two young men currently studying to be nurses, who had been orphaned to his care some years ago.

Unlike the frail children we'd seen in the city, Father's orphanage children had grown healthy on nutritious food and a stable and secure lifestyle. But, kids being kids, the generator-powered, trailer-sized clinic was a busy place, and with our doctors visiting, the clinic lines were long.

Through the open windows I could hear Matt's contagious laugh. He was having a grand time with a ticklish young boy while Gary concentrated on a little girl who sat as tall as she could, eyeball to eyeball, on the table. Throughout the exam, her rapt gaze never faltered and still looking at Gary over her shoulder, she nearly bumped into the doorway on her way out. She was smitten.

The clinic kept color-coded records of each child, used for following the treatments of diseases as simple as measles, and for tracking the effectiveness of drugs on children born to mothers with HIV. Looking through the record book I was struck by the enormous variety of handwriting. With doctors from all over the world visiting with bag in hand, it wasn't surprising.

That day alone, there were our docs and two dentists, Ron and Ronni from somewhere in the Midwest, adding their scrawls. They were a husband-wife team who came to Haiti for a month every year, bringing the mixed blessing of their service to abandoned children. Of their six grown children, five have already followed in their footsteps. Could compassion be genetic?

When I arrived the room was crowded already, with Gary and Matt, Father Rick and Malherbe and Ron and Ronni and each of their patients. Cabinets and shelves of supplies occupied both ends of the clinic, and two tables and an ancient dental chair consumed most of the center. Like the single desk in the room, every surface had something medical on it or under it.

A masked Ron and Ronni paused briefly over an open mouth — waiting for the next generator surge while I snapped a picture documenting the scene: dental instruments on a cloth-covered, wooden crate; a height measure, carved into the door jam; and dog-eared medical books stacked in boxes on the floor. It was a poor reflection of the sterling people who labored there, but for both, Father was eternally grateful.

As late afternoon clouds rolled against neighboring mountains, our team moved inside to dine with the staff in the conference room of the retreat Father had built a year ago. The building served as a brief getaway for the clergy who wallowed in the streets below and was home-away-from-home for orphanage volunteers. Father lived in one of the downstairs rooms and enjoyed the flow of visitors the new accommodations brought.

"Come see the downstairs," said Father Rick, adding that we'd better move quickly before the sun set and it got too dark.

The simple rooms were palatial by local standards, big enough for necessary bedroom furniture and a closet-sized bathroom of sink, toilet and shower. Heavy wool blankets took care of the chilly, mountain nights; candles tamed the dark.

Rick's apartment was scant bigger but naturally homier with his personal things placed about. It seemed crowded, but he dismissed with a wave the suggestion that it was too small for him and the work he needed to do.

"Oh, it's much better now," he said. "Kerosene and flashlight batteries are expensive, and I couldn't read by candlelight for very long. Then I heard about this." He held up a clear, glass pitcher of water and proudly placed it on the stone mantle of his fireplace.

"Put a candle behind the pitcher and, like magic, the flame is magnified. It lights the whole room evenly and I can read for hours," he beamed. Waste not, want not...leverage everything...think outside the box... I believed this man could squeeze blood out of a turnip.

Looking through his window to the magnificent view of terraced plots and latticed paths, we thought it a most beautiful stroke of luck that found Father Wasson in the right place at the right time for all the members of his growing family.

We returned upstairs for dessert of pecan pie, baked by Sister Philomena and just delivered by one of the staff from St. Damien's.

In the dark, beyond the candlelit room, we heard the German Shepherd guard dogs barking. As orphanage sentries they roamed the property at night, sniffing for intruders. Behind the retreat, a large, Rottweiler-mix dog paced along his chain. He was the enforcer; a known deterrent among those who didn't belong. I'd had the accidental pleasure of meeting him earlier and respected his low, menacing growl.

A candlelight Mass followed the candlelight dinner. Circled about the altar and readied by the taped cathedral music, we began the entrance hymn. Father raised his arms in welcome, to which one of the Shepherds pushed through the door and joined our choir. Out the dog went, and solemnity resumed.

Looking around the flickering room, our faces mirrored the same appreciation for Father's frugal decorating talents that we'd seen before. A work in progress, the walls and ceiling waited patiently for the transient brush, while the simulated stained glass windows reflected the warmth of friends gathered. We held hands and prayed, sharing a spiritual union unique to people bound by a common cause.

At the end of Mass, Father snuffed the candles one by one, leaving each of us in our own spiritual world, wrapped timelessly in the dark. Listening to the sigh of the night, I felt humbled to be with people who so eloquently expressed themselves with a thousand good works.

Back to reality, we flash-lighted it to the orphanage gate we had entered. There, Father made preparations for our nighttime descent to the hospital. For safety, there would be two vehicles and cell phones at the ready.

Stories of an earlier hijacking attempt on our route prompted nervous assertions of belief in angels. In the silence between tales, we lulled to the rhythmic swish of windshield wipers as they cleared away the mountain mist. Straining to see beyond the headlights, Father said again what a difference cell phones had made in their lives. They were always on charge.

In time we dropped, without incident, to the steamy world below and I crawled into my clean hotel bed wondering if there would be nightmares replaying sea-level tragedies or dreams of Father's mountain family.

7

Gird Thy Loins

It is said that behind every great man is a great woman. For Father Rick, that woman is a bespectacled, 90-pound, 77-year-old bundle of energy named Sister Philomena. Every picture I took of her came out blurred. She was Father Rick's straight man, the Amos to his Andy and the spice of his life. The good Sister fattened his belly with her home made sweets as easily as she snapped back with disapproval of his gluttony. Unafraid to disagree with the towering priest, Sister displayed a feistiness born of familiarity. No topic was sacred, and the match, equal. Such a pity their exchanges weren't recorded on tape.

"Sister is very modest," he said, grinning. "The Good Lord in his wisdom knows that. He only sends her afflictions below the knees."

As Sister fidgeted with the folds of her habit, Father continued with the story of the abscess on her leg and how she objected to his ultrasound. She finally acquiesced and bundled her skirt tightly around her knees for the exam. Even Father had to be sensitive to her station and generation-driven modesty. Procedure finished, he prescribed aspirin for her — and Valium for himself.

"Humph," she grunted, "He only talks that way when other people are around."

Father's jovial and oft-repeated suggestions that they should marry, were always met with an indignant, "Oh, Pater!" delivered with piercing eyes over gold-rimmed spectacles.

We clearly understood that Rick enjoyed exposing his fearless and impish side, but his occasional bawdy humor suggested that his mother must have had her hands full. So to, did Sister Philomena.

"If he were my husband, I'd never let him get away with some of the things he does!"

Returning seven years ago to her beloved Haitian babies, Sister Philomena Perreault had scrapped her Seattle retirement to assume duties at St. Damien's. Since 1988, she had been in charge of Kay Philomene, the "baby house" at St. Helene's Orphanage, so her retirement work at the pediatric hospital followed nicely her previous 24 years of volunteer service to children. Dressed in the ankle-length, white habit of her order, the tiny Sister traveled happily as nurse and friend for Father Rick as he made his rounds. By his side she felt safe, giving little thought to the recent shooting murder of a nun just leaving her compound.

Equally pleased to accompany our team on Friday, Sister agreed to assist Dr. Matt at another Sisters of Charity facility known as the Wound Clinic. Bouncing along in the front seat of the truck, back support pillow in place, she charmed us with her observations and the easy banter between priest and nun we'd come to expect.

At some point she asked, "Father, with such a nice name like Matthew, why would he call himself 'Matt'?"

"I don't know, Phil," grinned Father Rick.

Traffic on the two-lane road slowed with the arterial mergings common in the early morning. Normally zipping down that familiar stretch, the delay let us appreciate the roadside people readying their stalls for the day's commerce. Less touristy, their market was the stuff of daily life: shoe repair, tinwork, chickens in cages (for cock fights or dinner?) and bundles of firewood. One of the chickens badly pecked its surprised captor, who ranted threats easily understood in any language. The bird squawked back with fire in his eye and we laughed.

But not for long. Creole words shouted from a small crowd along the road caught Father's attention. He pulled over, grabbed his bag and motioned for the other docs to follow.

"Someone's hurt," he said over his shoulder.

They ran to join him over the embankment. The rest of us waited in the truck just a short time. Very soon they climbed from the brush and returned in a walk.

"She is dead," Father said, grasping the steering wheel. "Her family will come looking and find her." Maybe.

Back in the herd of traffic, the slow pace had another advantage. It made the road bumps easier for those in the back to anticipate. We continued our surveillance of city life. Whole neighborhoods of disaster-relief candidates rose from the dirt. Survivors of countless weather assaults, their owners had abandoned any pretext of repair, or, heaven forbid, paint. In the drabness, we saw naked toddlers stumble from open doorways to a playground waiting to bite. Chunks of dirty coral and iron scraps jumbled with rubble that filled every open space.

In a hurricane the winds fling tin roofs everywhere, slicing bodies and buildings alike. I imagined torrents of water rushing through the hovels, churning rusty car parts and earth into sharp and dangerous weapons. People caught in its path would seldom emerge unscathed as it headed for the corridors that pass for roads. Turning prickly and uneven when dried, the trafficked surface jolted cars to pieces and shredded the thousands of tires that littered the city.

Women crouched in the dirt on haunches, skirts tucked modestly between their legs as they tended coals under round-bottom pots. Meals, we were told, when food is had, are cooked in hot oil, in pots precariously perched above charcoal pits. Given the proximity of human flesh, burns were common. Along the roads, venders hawking skewers of mystery meat, cooked on mobile braziers, were equally vulnerable with the ever-moving throng.

In the market part of town, as pedestrians passed crawling cars, the commercial side of Haiti emerged. It was your basic merchant review of goods for sale, evenly distributed between stalls and the more mobile baskets balanced on heads.

Sister Philomena leaned from her window and traded a coin for dried bananas, cautioning, "They're sweet but you'd better scrape off the salt or it will make you thirsty."

As if on cue, those in the back hailed a boy selling pop. Father hoped the bottles weren't frozen, noting that sometimes a sticky mess would burst out. I couldn't imagine it would take long to thaw in the heat anyway, and a cold bottle on the neck was heaven. Sister had her arm hanging out the window for buying on the go and was watching so intently for ripe tangerines that she almost lost the rest of her money to a passing beggar.

There were many such characters, the fallout of Haiti's 75 percent unemployment rate. With an average daily income of less than $2, most had no other choice. Starvation was the handy whip of thievery.

Sister's incident seemed appropriate for the location. We had come upon a place given an ominous Creole name that roughly translated to "Meat Crossing." Centuries ago, hundreds of thousands of African slaves had passed through the market to be inspected and sold. Predictably, the heavy lash sparked a rebellion that created the first modern black republic. Freedom and Democracy not withstanding, their descendants had yet to benefit.

All manner of goods, from baskets of squawking chickens to cases of Coke, balanced on the heads of people on the move. Men maneuvered heavily laden, two-wheeled carts through peopled streets, bumping and scraping their way past honeycombed market stalls and threading streams of overloaded, honking Tap-Taps. Currents of people, proceeding in a slow, undulating ripple of movement, paused briefly at intersections. With no stoplights, vehicles and people tended to create interesting ebbs and flows only appreciated from a bird's-eye view; and everywhere, the potential for injury. It's no wonder wound clinics do a brisk business.

Passing through an especially crowded area we saw children and adults dart beneath the outstretched arm of a backhoe, hard at the business of demolishing a building. Like buzzards on a carcass, they supplanted any thought of a clean up crew, scavenging bits of rebar, bricks, anything that could be sold or transformed to useful.

Judging from the twisted and rusty wire that held almost everything together, the repair material had more lives than a cat. New construction in Haiti isn't much of an improvement, with homemade ladders (bound with wire), buckets on ropes and flimsy branches used for floor supports. Most of the workers had shoes but no hardhats. After all, safety was not much of a priority when you're starving.

"Look there," Father Rick said, pointing from the pickup at a legless man on a corner. The man raised his hand in greeting. "You should have seen his face when I drove by last month and gave him five thousand gourds. He never forgets to wave now."

Rick explained that after a funeral, someone had slipped him the gourds (about a thousand Haitian dollars or $350 U.S.) as a memorial donation and asked that he give it to whoever really needed it.

"On my way home I saw the man begging and wanted to give him a lucky day. I stopped the car, got out, placed it in his hand, got back in the car and drove away," he chuckled, the corners of his eyes crinkling. The impulse was no less delightful in the telling.

The alleyway to the Sisters of Charity Wound Clinic lay beyond a wall of tables, heavy with housewares and bolts of bright fabric. The green cross on the windshield appeared to be our ticket as a turbaned lady smiled and moved into action, directing her neighbors to clear the way. The sharp turn to avoid some goods still on the ground made the vehicle's tie rods screech in objection. The clinic's gatekeepers turned and waved in recognition.

Anxious dark eyes followed as the six of us piled out of the crew cab to join Matt, Debbie, Gary and Astrid in front of the clinic. After their bumpy ride in the open pickup, the four were relieved to be upright. Once inside the tall, iron gate, we stepped gingerly through a carpet of waiting patients and made our way to a warehouse-sized room, lined with occupied benches. Dr. Matt and Sister Philomena stationed themselves on stools in the center of the room while Dr. Gary and Astrid found space and some crates nearby. Dr. Malherbe and Father manned the operating areas in an adjoining building as Sister Alice Mary, Sister Agnes Anne, Annette and I replaced other nuns and staff in the wound clinic.

Clinic. The word conjures white walls, padded exam tables and sterile everything. Not so in Haiti where the resourceful survive and nothing goes wasted. I passed a Sister carefully cutting the cotton stuffing from pill bottles into swabs. In the corner were stacks of "pill packets," little envelopes made from newspaper and magazine pages, folded to hold medications dispensed from quart and gallon-sized supply bottles. Even the vellum wrappings from sterile gauze pads were stacked and saved for who knows what. This was a place where trash was treasure.

The open causeway between the buildings was crammed with men, women and children whose wounds could be smelled before seen. Nothing in my experience as mom had prepared me for this. Patients sat three at a time along a grimy bench to prop injured legs on stools draped with small pieces of Betadine stained plastic. Sister Alice Mary called the procedure of wound cleaning "debriding," but it was torture none-the-less.

Clamps and scissors rested spread-eagled in shallow trays of alcohol, competing with buckets of gauze, cotton balls and homemade rolls of bandages for space on the small table nearby. White-robed Sisters in blue aprons floated among our designated pods, organizing scant medical supplies on shelves that doubled as room dividers. We took the offered blue aprons and donned latex gloves for the work ahead.

"Any time now," said Sister Alice Mary as she cut away the dead skin from her first patient's leg. She nodded at the man next in line.

Annette and I watched for a minute, took a deep breath and jumped right in. As a child, I had instinctively held my breath when walking past anyone who looked like they were sick or might smell bad, as if protecting my lungs from invasion. Looking at the line of patients, I thought, "I can't hold my breath that long." Dressed in blue scrubs, apron and gloves, we looked like we knew what we were doing, and by the end of the morning, we did.

My first patient was a man with an ugly, open leg wound, crusted over with dead tissue and weeping out the sides. In copycat fashion, I soaked and peeled and dropped the dead skin into the rapidly filling wastebasket the three of us shared. He never flinched and I kept my breakfast.

Next in line was a little girl about seven, with anxious eyes and a burn that crossed her cheek, into her nose. Again, the scrubbing and peeling as Sister had shown, until healthy skin showed through. Her pretty face would be scarred no matter what anyone did, but I felt guilty anyway. The child cried out now and then and clung to her mother, but there were no tears. What ran down my cheeks was sweat I dared not wipe with tainted gloves.

Annette and I shared the next patient, a man whose wound hadn't been cleaned for weeks.

In the heat, the smell of gangrene floated through the bandage that stuck to his skin, and I turned to the supply table behind us for a moment's relief. We soaked and peeled and cut away the rotting cloth, exposing an ugly wound from ankle to knee. Annette swabbed, peeled and cut what she could, slathered the wound with antiseptic salve and bound his leg carefully. We knew the "debriding" would not be enough, but we did what we could with what we had, and moved on.

Before we had left Boise, Annette had told us about the advice her traveled son had given her. Confirming that the Haiti trip would be a great experience, he suggested she not hang around the hotel but "get out and mingle with the people." Up to our armpits at that very moment, we remembered his admonition and had a good laugh.

In medicine there must be a fine line between efficiency and tenderness. With the sheer numbers of people needing attention, Annette and I struggled with our inexperience in hurrying to end the pain we were causing, or keeping at it to remove all the infection. It was easier to do the latter with stoic adults, but the cries of the children were a different matter.

In the next room, Sister Philomena was caught in her own personal agony as Dr. Matt's interpreter in STD (Sexually Transmitted Diseases) cases. More accustomed to diaper rash and childhood diseases, she was a bundle of conflicted emotions.

"Oh Dr. Matt, please don't ask me to do another one of those sex cases again," she pleaded. Her very real distress was only more fuel for future, good-natured jokes.

That day our little team treated over two hundred men, women and children for ailments from malnutrition to cancer. Hot oil burns, common among adults, were most pitiful on the children. Napping babies, victims of overturned pots, clung to mothers who were blistered no less in the rescue. Gashes, left untended until it was almost too late, were treated with salve and a heavy dose of hope. In some cases that was all we could do.

The sun, straight overhead, beat down on the squirming line of remaining patients who looked glumly at the Sister just closing the wound clinic. Though we worked as quickly as we could, the allotted time had expired and the balance would have to suffer through a new line tomorrow.

Damp from our work, we peeled gloves and aired our wrinkled hands as we followed Sister Alice Mary to our next assignment. The stethoscope slung around her neck chaffed visibly as she prepared an IV for the young man intently listening to Father. Anesthetic was needed to see him through a painful but simple procedure, and our job was to hold him on the gurney and tend him as he came to.

Meanwhile, Dr. Malherbe commissioned me to help with an infant needing surgery in the next room. I tied her IV bottle to the mesh on the window and readied her arm for the IV. A piece of folded cardboard ripped from a medical supply box stabilized her arm and I secured the extension with narrow strips of tape, wider than her incredibly tiny hand. She quieted, limp as a rag doll on the battered table, and Malherbe began his work. Called back to Sister Alice Mary and Annette, I missed watching the delicate surgery progress.

The young man lingered understandably in his drugged haze, breathing the sleep of a child, reluctant to reenter grinding reality. Holding his head to the side as instructed, I looked down at his subjugated person and couldn't blame him.

He finally roused. Annette removed the IV and we helped him pull on his worn, soiled pants and sneakers without laces. Carefully guiding him like outriggers, we sat him in the narrow causeway that had been vacated by the disappointed wound patients. The close space had become a virtual oven. Father called for some water to give the man a pill and Annette obliged from her own bottle. We couldn't believe no one else had water. She gave him a second drink.

Freed from our stained aprons, we peeled a second pair of gloves, swathed our hands and arms with antiseptic hand wash and shifted attention to the pill dispensary in the main room. The good Sisters filled each prescription precisely, counting and dropping the color-specific tablets into pre-folded, reading material packets, and poring lotion from huge jugs into smaller, recycled plastic bottles. Vitamins and iron pills were a casual affair: a dollop of this and a handful of that. We caught on quickly. I felt like an experienced cook, except the soup was people and the ingredients, often, just garnish.

Casually surveying the crowd, I connected with Gary and Matt who shrugged weary shoulders and looked a bit neutralized. Since day one, they'd said most of the physical problems they encountered were totally fixable in the U.S. In Haiti, all they could do for some of the patients was prescribe vitamins and lotion, which was next to useless for people who had nothing to eat.

The conveyor belt of children continued. Each new little patient felt the doctor's hand slide along gray, dry patches on arms and legs, telltale signs that the skin would eventually split open from lack of protein and hydration. The docs shook their heads at no one in particular. Starvation wasn't just a word for a rumbling stomach — it hurt and killed.

Climbing back in the truck, Sister Philomena confessed that she hadn't liked being there. "There were so many, Father. I don't like to see so many," she said, emphasizing the last word. Coming from the more protective and controlled environment of St. Damien's, Sister was only being honest.

Father's cell phone rang to announce a change of plans. The Brothers needed our group to follow up on three critical patients, among them the fellow with the broken back.

The pickup lurched the familiar route, and preceded by a dust devil, we crunched through the gate and stopped in the expected hush. It was quiet enough to hear a soul leave its body. The Brothers' faces, blank with fatigue, brightened as the team approached. It had been a long day for them and it wasn't over yet.

Flies speckled the white sheet covering a form on the cot nearest the door and two beds,

occupied the day before, were empty.
Matt and Gary set to work in the
shadows while Rick carried a bed-
pan to the refuse area beyond the
supply room. From 20 feet, even
Vic's rubbed in our nostrils couldn't
cover the stench. Rick emerged ashen-faced.

He was mortal after all.

Just before we left, Sister was told that the
blood sample she had taken earlier from a
young man, a stroke victim at the clinic, had
registered positive for HIV. His doe-eyed wife
stood next to him in the shade, fanning them
both with a piece of cardboard. Groaning,
Sister lowered her head and turned from our
group to give them the news.

Less animated than usual, Father concentrated on the traffic, which was slowed by a
sloshing water truck on a grind up the hill.
Profits spilling into the gutter, it lurched past a
dry jungle of people and their poor, parched
habitat. Beyond what I could see from roadside, I knew what was hidden was worse.

Goliath proportions of tuberculosis, hepatitis, AIDS and syphilis are spiraling in Haiti,
aggravated by rampant malnutrition and dehy-
dration. The state health care system seems
riddled with takers who siphon what they can

from foreign and sometimes private aid, making any benefit to the people improbable. Only small, private medical efforts appear to have any tangible merit, perhaps because their spiritual foundation focuses on the philosophy of a hands-on approach. I had always thought that that was what medicine was all about. It was disconcerting to see a medical community so polarized and paralyzed by greed. David-sized humanitarians would have to choose their stones well.

"All work and no play" being an unhealthy lifestyle, we determined to hit the shops and galleries before dinner. John and Sister Agnes Anne, skilled at bartering on local offerings, pointed us to a promising neighborhood of galleries and shops. On a solo quest in the opposite direction, John set off to buy two refrigerators for the lab.

Most of the colorful tourist fare looked alike — a dozen or so products, handmade by the zillions, most likely in sweat shops run by the government. Every street corner had them. Although the galleries had much better art, the only thing I might have wanted to bring home was the Chinese porcelain vase in our hotel room. Contemporary-primitive Haitian art and flashy, sequined Voodoo flags, though beautifully made, were cousins to the boxes of handicraft genre I'd stripped from our home in a downsizing fit the winter before. I was happy with my booty of Haitian food recipes, coffee, vanilla and rum.

Our only supper "out" had Father Rick and Sister Philomena at one end of a long restaurant table and Dr. Gautier at the other with Astrid, two hospital doctors and staff sprinkled among us. The full moon shone through carefully wrought iron panels and the open grill sizzled and flared in the corner. It smelled delicious.

Father Rick began with a short prayer of thanks and a series of long toasts that flushed our cheeks and made us laugh. Once again, Sister Philomena lowered her shaking head in embarrassment. I raised my glass and silently toasted him an Albert Sweitzer quote: "A man does not have to be an angel to be a saint."

Comforted that everything on the menu was safe to eat we eased into a memorable evening of joy and deepening connections. It was prelude to a bittersweet farewell.

8

...Said The Blind Man

The buckle tight across my lap, I closed my eyes to the Haitian sun reflected off the wing. We were headed home.

The week had gone quickly and put a new wrinkle in the adage, "Time flies when you're having fun." Rolls of film, packed between bags of fragrant coffee beans and Haitian vanilla, would tell only part of the story.

Engines whined, drowning out the clicks of other passengers' belts, and I settled back, inhaling shallow breaths of stale airplane air and feeling grateful for the improvement. Unlike other heavy-lidded taxi-ing, the yaw and pitch of the tarmac ride lent a certain edginess to my dilemma. It was an unsteady feeling, not unlike a dream where you feel you have to run and your feet won't move. How could I translate for people back home, incredible experiences and powerful moments, seen with and without a viewfinder?

I was unconsciously chewing the inside of my lip when the plane stopped, made its sweeping turn for the take off and powered forward. Random vignettes of Haiti continued.

There was the black face of a woman setting her jaw to the day's bucket of water on her head; the man in rags pulling an impossibly loaded cart through crushing traffic; the naked toddler beating off a dog from a morsel of food. Their faces may have had the drawn expression of patience that comes from adversity long suffered, but that was not all.

Like the helper at the clinic, they had the patina of having endured with the wisdom of generations in their blood. They had been bred of a thousand ancestors who survived, clinging to thoughts of freedom and winning democracy with their lives. Torn from their lands and families, stripped of their roots, they melded their nature-centered deities with imposed Christian saints to form a hybrid religion. It was that spirit which had promised to sustain them through the trial of greed that visits every country.

Exploited by outsiders since Columbus landed in 1492, the Haiti we saw five hundred years later was rotting from the inside out. Beyond food and water, what the people lacked most was opportunity, tantalizingly kept at bay by their country's unlegislated Apartheid, contagious corruption and a host of other reasons. How much longer would the collective results of her abuse, parading daily through her streets and bulging from her sewers, continue? The world was asking.

We knew there were no answers for the masses, but that was no excuse to do nothing. In a country where foreign aid is more apt to line the pockets of the privileged, it's best to be focused on what *can* be done.

Father Frechette and the network of volunteers we left behind do good work in the seething caldron of Haiti, giving dignity and love to helpless children and the dying. They do it one day at a time, one moment at a time, one person at a time. For them, the miracle of touch is real. For the rest of us, the challenge is to help.

Its landing gear safely tucked away, the plane banked north. I opened my eyes to slow motion visions against the blue sky, and saw a few of the lucky ones: the tiny child sitting forlorn on a green hospital chair, sucking in short, sharp breaths and wearing the same expression of any toddler who wants his Mommy; the bubble-blowing orphans, their faces wide with white, white teeth. Busy classroom scenes, and noisy playgrounds and the impish grin of a teasing girl floated by. And, once more, I saw

Francesca and the face of Markison at that res-
urrection-moment with Sister Lorraine.

The plane leveled off and with a tightness in
my throat, I looked across the aisle to my
teammates, hoping for a distraction to stifle
the coming wave. Too late on the uptake, my
eyes grew hot and blurry with thoughts of
Father Rick and Sister Philomena, Astrid, the
Sisters and Brothers, the Rons and Ronnis of
the world, and I turned away, deeply, irrevoca-
bly, profoundly humbled.

* * *

Haiti and "Project Haiti" Background

Haiti's troubled history began with Columbus's discovery of the island he named Hispanola in 1492. Spanish Conquistadors and later the French rapidly stripped the island's lush forests to grow crops destined for Europe. With no immunity to the white man's diseases, the Arawak natives soon perished and West African slaves were imported to work the land.

In 1697, the western half of the island was ceded to the French from Spain and renamed Saint-Dominque. One hundred years later the colony's population had grown to over 600,000 black slaves, 35,000 mulattos and only 25,000 whites. While the slave-holding system produced an agricultural-rich colony, it created great internal class and color conflicts. Influenced by the French and American revolutions and with American and British help, the brutalized slaves revolted to defeat Napoleon's formidable army sent to quell the rebellion. Over 350,000 were killed.

The surviving slaves proudly formed the second republic in the Western Hemisphere, but although their descendants eventually accounted for the bulk of Haiti's population, true democracy eluded them. For the next 200 years, corrupt leadership accompanied by a series of dictators culminating with the infamous Papa Doc Duvialier and his son, who was overthrown by a military coup. The rest of the Caribbean distanced itself from the problematic country, and few offshore investors materialized to help modernize the country.

In 1989, the popular priest, Jean-Bertrand Aristide was elected president of Haiti, but was shortly toppled by another coup. Restored to power by United States intervention, Aristide's administration has had little impact on the rampant corruption that siphoned off financial aid from countries and the well-intentioned abroad.

Father William Wasson, whose organization, *Our Little Brothers and Sisters*, had successfully established numerous orphanages in Mexico and Central America, found a need in Haiti. In 1988, he asked Father Rick Frechette, CP to start an orphanage there, and with help from Sister Virginia McMonagle, R.S.C.J., and the San Diego "Friends of Father Wasson's Orphans," the facility became a reality. Soon to follow was a 100-bed pediatric care center, known now as St. Damien's Hospital, which met the health needs of the children of the orphanage and Port-au-Prince.

Saint Alphonsus Foundation became involved in the effort when Rob and Betsy Luce met Father Rick and Sister Virginia while adopting their son, Parker from Haiti. Rob, a Foundation board member, saw that the medical staff at St. Damien's had to do their work without access to x-ray, ultrasound, lab equipment and many critical drugs. He brought the needs of Father Rick to Saint Alphonsus Vice President, Carolyn Stafford Pratt, and in 1995 "Project Haiti" was launched.

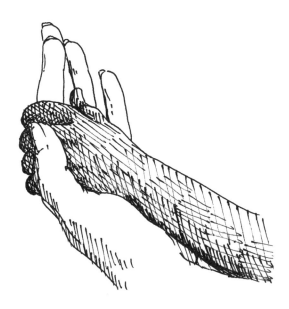

How To Help

Project Haiti exists on modest donations. We like it that way for two reasons: (1) we want to encourage everyone to help a little bit, burdening no one, and (2) we want to solve the small problems, not the huge ones, one child, one person at a time.

Like the single touch that means so much, we know that every dollar, every item, every effort our mission teams make, goes a long way to alleviate the suffering described in the book, *Touching Haiti*. We hope you'll join us.

Your contribution is tax deductible.

The amount may be small,
but the meaning is immense.

Send your gifts to:
Project Haiti
Saint Alphonsus Foundation
1055 North Curtis Road, Boise, ID 83706

Make checks payable to: Project Haiti

Credit Card Donations: (208) 367-2759
Online donations:
http://www.sarmc.org/giving/projects.html